Lesson & Theory
ALL-IN
LEVEL 2A

PIANO

Adventures® *by Nancy and Randall Faber*
THE BASIC PIANO METHOD

This book belongs to: ⎯⎯⎯⎯⎯⎯⎯⎯⎯⎯⎯⎯⎯⎯⎯⎯⎯⎯⎯⎯⎯⎯⎯⎯⎯⎯⎯

Production Coordinator: Jon Ophoff
Cover and Illustrations: Terpstra Design, San Francisco
Engraving: Dovetree Productions, Inc.

Book Only ISBN 978-1-61677-652-7
Book & CD ISBN 978-1-61677-653-4

Progress Chart

Keep track of your progress.
Colour or put a star sticker for each item.

		Lesson & Theory	Technique & Performance
☆	Get Ready for Take-off! (Level 1 Review)	4-5	
☆	Note Reading Guide	6-7	
☆	When the Saints Go Marching In	8-9	4

UNIT 1 Quavers

☆	Quavers	10	
☆	Famous People	11	4, 6-7
☆	Skip to My Lou, THEORY: Fiddle to My Quavers	12-13	5, 8
☆	Leftover Popcorn, THEORY: The Popcorn Bowl	14-15	9
☆	A Minuet for Mr. Bach's Children	16-17	
☆	THEORY: A Jazzy Song for Mr. Bach	18-19	
☆	Mr. Brahms' Famous Lullaby	20-21	10-11
☆	THEORY: Mr. Brahms' Time Signature Game, Eye-Training/Ear-Training	22-23	

UNIT 2 Transposition

☆	Ice Cream and More Ice Cream	24	5, 12
☆	Mr. Haydn's Theme	25	
☆	THEORY: Eye-Training with Haydn	26	
☆	THEORY: Ear-Training with Bach, Beethoven, and Brahms	27	
☆	My Daydream	28-29	5
☆	The Clock Strikes Thirteen!	30	13
☆	The Elf's Silver Hammer	31	14-17
☆	THEORY: Crescendo and Diminuendo, Eye-Training/Ear-Training	32-33	

UNIT 3 The Phrase

☆	Ode to Joy	34-35	18
☆	I Am the King	36	19
☆	THEORY: I Am the Phrase Finder!	37	
☆	Moonlight Melody	38	20-21
☆	THEORY: You Can Compose!	39	

UNIT 4 Semitones and Tones

☆	THEORY: The Puppet Show, Playful Puppets	40-41	
☆	Our Detective Agency	42-43	22
☆	Storms on Saturn	44-45	23, 24-25
☆	THEORY: Moon Shadows Improv, Planets and Moons	46-47	

Get Ready for Take-off!
(Level 1 Review)

- Connect each note to its matching rest.

- Draw bar lines for this time signature.
- Write *1 2 3 4* under the correct beats. Then play the rhythm using a C chord.

- Draw bar lines for this time signature.
- Write *1 2 3* under the correct beats. Then play the rhythm using a G chord.

- Draw a line connecting each musical term to the correct place in the music.

G clef, or treble clef   2nd   3rd   4th   5th   double bar line

time signature   accent mark

semibreve rest   crotchet rest

mezzo piano   minim rest

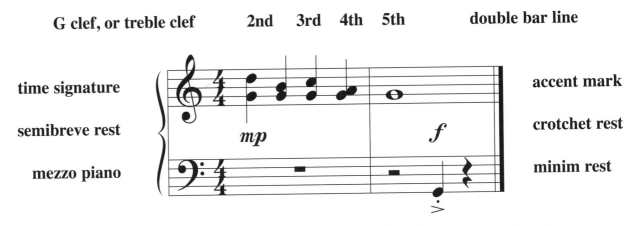

F clef, or bass clef   forte   bar line   staccato

THEORY

- Put a ✔ on the correct key from the ✗.

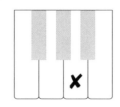

UP a semitone   DOWN a semitone

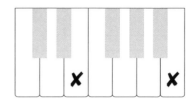

UP a semitone   DOWN a semitone

- Circle **tonic** (step 1) or **dominant** (step 5) for the shaded note.

C 5-Finger Scale

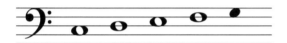

tonic / dominant

C 5-Finger Scale

tonic / dominant

G 5-Finger Scale

tonic / dominant

G 5-Finger Scale

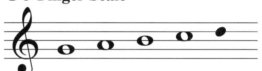

tonic / dominant

- Play these **I** and **V7** chords:

C 5-Finger Scale

I   V7   I

G 5-Finger Scale

I   V7   I

SYMBOLS AND TERMS

- Connect each term to its correct definition.

legato

staccato

ritard.

sharp

flat

- Up a semitone
- Smooth, connected
- Detached, lift quickly
- Gradually slow down
- Down a semitone

5

Treble Clef Note Reading Guide

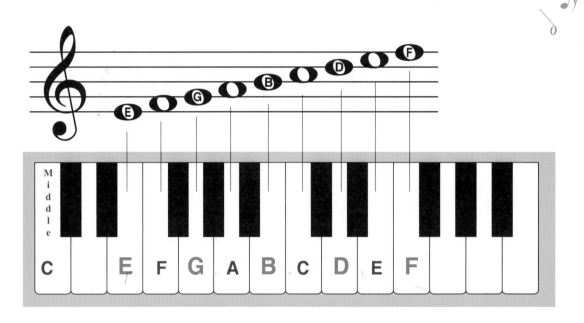

Exercise 1 by Memory
- Say the LINE notes quickly 3 times.
- Say the SPACE notes quickly 3 times.

Exercise 2
- Play E-G-B-D-F on the piano 2 times.
- Play the F-A-C-E spaces on the piano 2 times.

Exercise 3
- Your teacher will say, "Line 2," or "Line 5," etc. How fast can you play and say the note?
- Repeat with space notes. For example, "Space 2," or "Space 4," etc.

Exercise 4
- Darken the LINE notes to hide the letters.
- Your teacher will point to any LINE or SPACE note. Play and say it on the piano.

Exercise 5
- Name and play these notes. Repeat at many lessons.

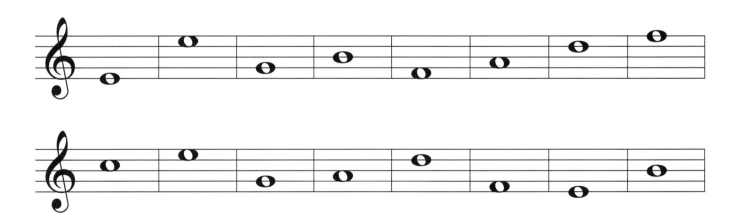

Teacher Note: Do these reading activities throughout this level. Regular review will develop confident note readers.

Bass Clef Note Reading Guide

Exercise 1
- Your teacher will point to a "smart note"—Bass G, Middle D, or Top Line A. How fast can you play and say it?
- Now find and play LINE notes B and F.

Exercise 2
- Are you ready for a challenge? Darken all the line notes.
- Your teacher will point to any bass clef LINE note. Play and say it on the piano.

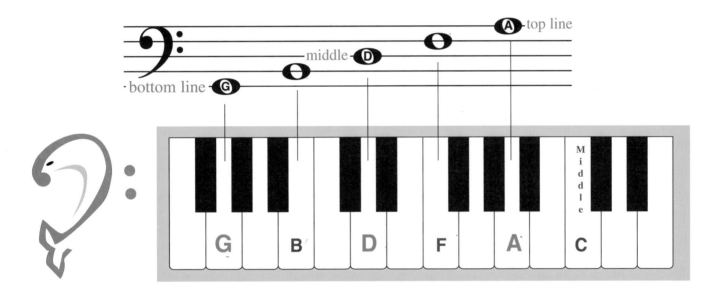

Exercise 3
- Name and play these notes. When needed, think, "What is the closest smart note?" Then move up or down. Repeat at many lessons.

Review Piece

Rhythm Hint: This piece begins with an incomplete bar on beat 2.

These 3 notes are called **upbeats**, **pick-up notes** or an **anacrusis**. They lead into the first full bar.

- Look at the final bar and circle the missing beat?

When the Saints Go Marching In

G 5-Finger Scale

> **Review:** A **slur** is a curved line that means to play *legato* (connected).

Brightly   **Traditional**

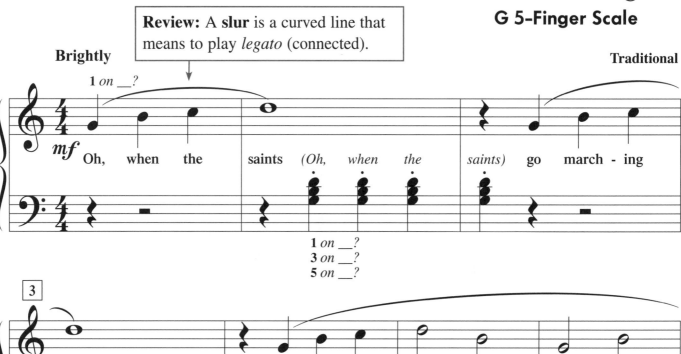

Teacher Duet: (Student plays *1 octave higher*)

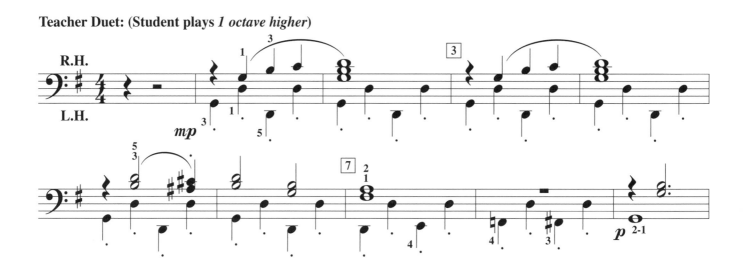

DISCOVERY Find a **I** and **V7** chord in this piece.

9

Quavers
(Eighth Notes)

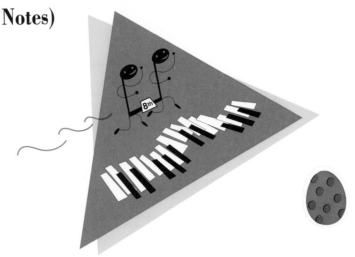

2 quavers equal a crotchet

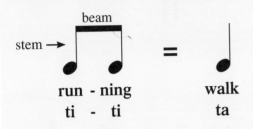

run - ning   walk
ti - ti   ta

Think of quavers as *running* notes.

- Tap and count these rhythms with your teacher.
- Now write **1 2 3 4** under the correct beats. Your teacher will help you.

1.
walk   run - ning walk   run - ning   walk   run - ning walk   walk
ta   ti - ti   ta   ti - ti   ta   ti - ti   ta   ta
Ex.   **1**   **2**   **3**   **4**

2.
run - ning walk   run - ning walk   run - ning walk   walk   walk
ti - ti   ta   ti - ti   ta   ti - ti   ta   ta   ta

3.
run - ning run - ning walk   walk   run - ning run - ning walk   walk
ti - ti - ti - ti   ta   ta   ti - ti - ti - ti   ta   ta

Quaver Patterns

1. Circle this pattern in
   RHYTHM 1 above.
   Play on a G chord.

2. Circle this pattern in
   RHYTHM 2 above.
   Play on a C chord.

3. Circle this pattern in
   RHYTHM 3 above.
   Play on a G chord.

Famous People

_____ 5-Finger Scale

With a strong beat

1 on __?

f Sing the names of fa - mous peo - ple:

3

1 on __?

Em - i - ly Bron - të, Ben - ja - min Brit - ten,

5

Chris - to - pher Co - lum - bus, A - ma - de - us Mo - zart,

7

Rob - in Hood, San - ta Claus, Pe - ter Pan, Jack Frost, Cin - der - el - la, too!

DISCOVERY Play *Famous People* with the metronome ticking at ♩ = **112**.

Teacher Duet: (Student plays *1 octave higher*)

R.H.

L.H. *mf*

C B = C B

← Middle C line

Skip to My Lou

_____ **5-Finger Scale**

- Write **I** or **V7** below each L.H. chord.

Happily

3 *on __?*

Swing your part - ner, skip to my Lou.

Ex. **I**

5

move ① *to B*

Swing your part - ner, skip to my Lou. Swing your part - ner,

2

skip to my Lou. Skip to my Lou, my dar - ling.

1

DISCOVERY Play the R.H. melody and change the rhythm to fit these familiar verses:

Verse 1: *Pigs in the Parlour, shoo fly shoo!* (♩ ♫ ♩ ♩ | ♩ ♩ ♩)

Verse 2: *Flies in the buttermilk, shoo fly shoo!* (♩ ♫ ♫ ♩ | ♩ ♩ ♩)

Teacher Duet: (Student plays *1 octave higher*)

R.H.

L.H.

🎵 CD 6-7   ✋ Tech & Perf pages 5 (Dancing Thumb), 8

Fiddle to My Quavers

1. Draw only **one note** in the blank violin to equal the **quavers** of the first violin.

2. Each fiddler's rhythm below is incomplete.

• Complete each bar with ONLY pairs of **quavers**.

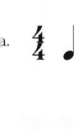

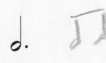

13

A **natural** cancels a sharp or a flat.

A natural will always be a white key.

- Circle the natural below.

Leftover Popcorn

Words by
Jennifer MacLean

Cheerfully

shift ① to B

mp

Left - o - ver pop - corn ly - ing in the bowl, I like pop - corn
Got up so ear - ly just so I could eat last night's pop - corn,

(prepare L.H.)

1 *on* __?
2 *on* __?

4   shift back to C
                    ①

one day old. But what do I see? Just my bad luck!
what a treat! But what do I see? Just my bad luck!

7

f

Ma - ma fed the pop - corn to the duck!

CREATIVE With R.H. only, make this piece longer by repeating the last line in different octaves.

Teacher Duet: (Student plays *1 octave higher*)

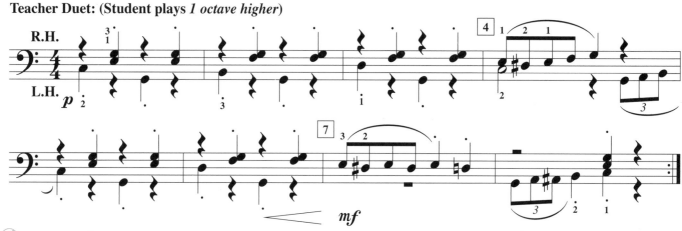

R.H.

L.H. *p*

4

7

mf

14   CD 8-9   Tech & Perf page 9

The Natural ♮

A natural cancels a sharp or flat. A natural will **always be a white key**.

The Popcorn Bowl

1.
- Circle each **natural** ♮ in the music below.
- Now sightread the melody.

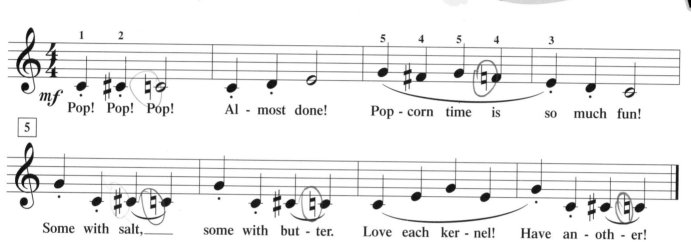

2. Put a ✓ on the correct key to match each popcorn kernel below.

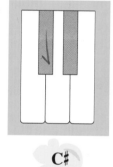 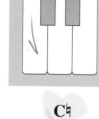 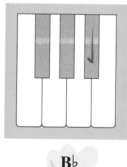 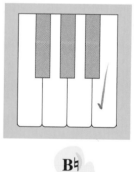

C♯   C♮   B♭   B♮

3. A natural can be on a **line** or in a **space**.

- Trace these naturals.
  Hint: Draw an "L," then a "7."

 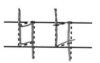

4.
- Trace each natural. Then draw another natural beside the one you traced.
- Trace each natural. Then draw another natural beside the one you traced.

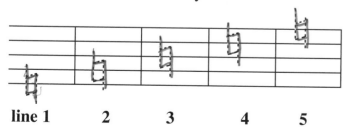

line 1   2   3   4   5

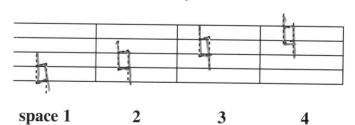

space 1   2   3   4

15

Minuet — a dance that is always in $\frac{3}{4}$ time.
This minuet uses this rhythm pattern over and over.

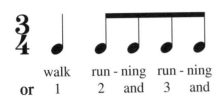

$\frac{3}{4}$	walk	run - ning	run - ning
or	1	2 and	3 and

Practice Steps

- Put a ✓ over each bar with the rhythm pattern shown above.
- Clap this piece with your teacher.

A Minuet for
Mr. Bach's Children

Quavers split
between the hands

from the *Notebook*
for Anna Magdalena Bach
arranged

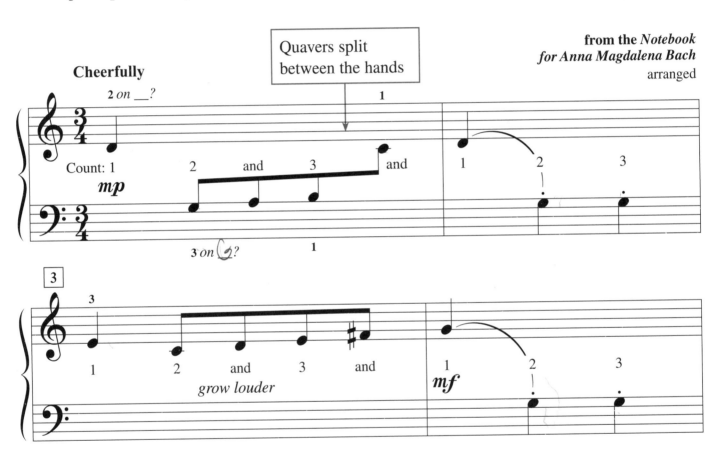

Teacher Duet: (Student plays *1 octave higher*)

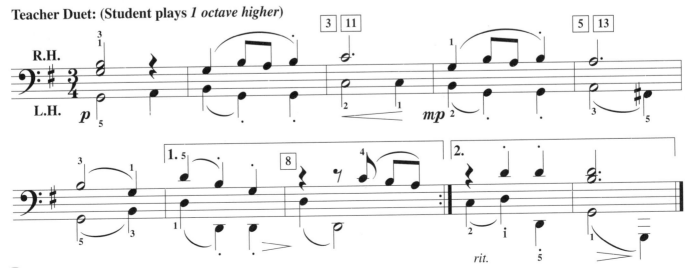

Anna Magdalena Bach's Special Notebook

Mr. Johann Sebastian Bach (1685-1750, Germany) had a large family—20 children!
The Bach family had a special notebook filled with music written by the family
and friends.

Bach presented this music notebook to his wife Anna Magdalena as a gift. Anna
Magdalena's initials and the year 1725 were printed in gold on light green paper. This
minuet is one of the most famous selections.

Though Bach's music is over 250 years old, it has influenced all kinds of music—from choir music to pop sounds of today. Here, Bach's minuet is changed into a "pop" song.

- Add bar lines after every **4 beats**.
  Notice the time signature changed from $\frac{3}{4}$ to $\frac{4}{4}$.

- Write 1 - 2 - 3 - 4 for the correct beats in *bars 1-7*.

- Play with the teacher duet.
  Which version of Bach's melody do you like the best?

A Jazzy Song for Mr. Bach

from the Notebook for Anna Magdalena Bach
arranged by Nancy Faber

Cheerfully

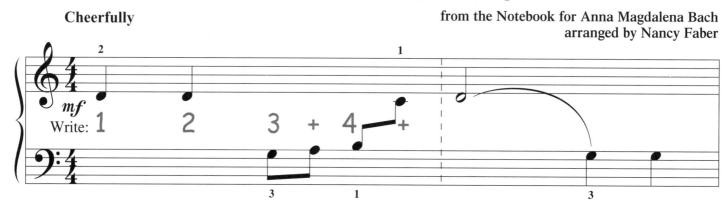

Teacher Duet: (Student plays *1 octave higher*)

Did you know...

Bach was orphaned at age 9.

Bach walked over 200 miles to hear an organ concert.

Bach composed over 1000 works in his lifetime.

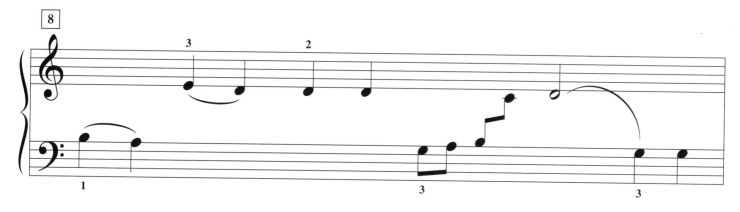

Your teacher will play Bach's melody in 3/4 or 4/4 time. Listen carefully and name the **time signature**! Do this several times.

19

Review: The Sustaining Pedal

The right-foot pedal on the piano is called the **sustaining pedal**. This pedal lifts the *dampers* (felts) off the strings, which lets the sounds continue to ring/sustain.

The symbol below tells you when to use the sustaining pedal.

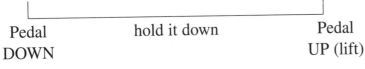

Pedal
DOWN

hold it down

Pedal
UP (lift)

Mr. Brahms' Famous Lullaby

Johannes Brahms
(1833–1897, Germany)
arranged

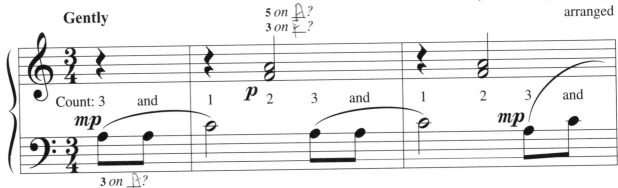

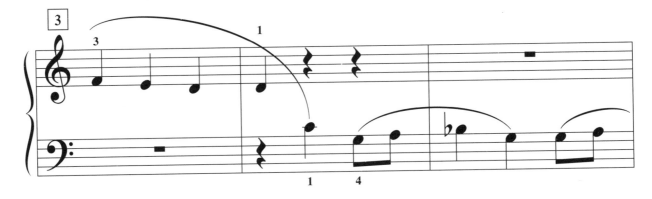

Teacher Duet: (Student plays *1 octave higher*)

CD 12-13   Tech & Perf pages 10-11

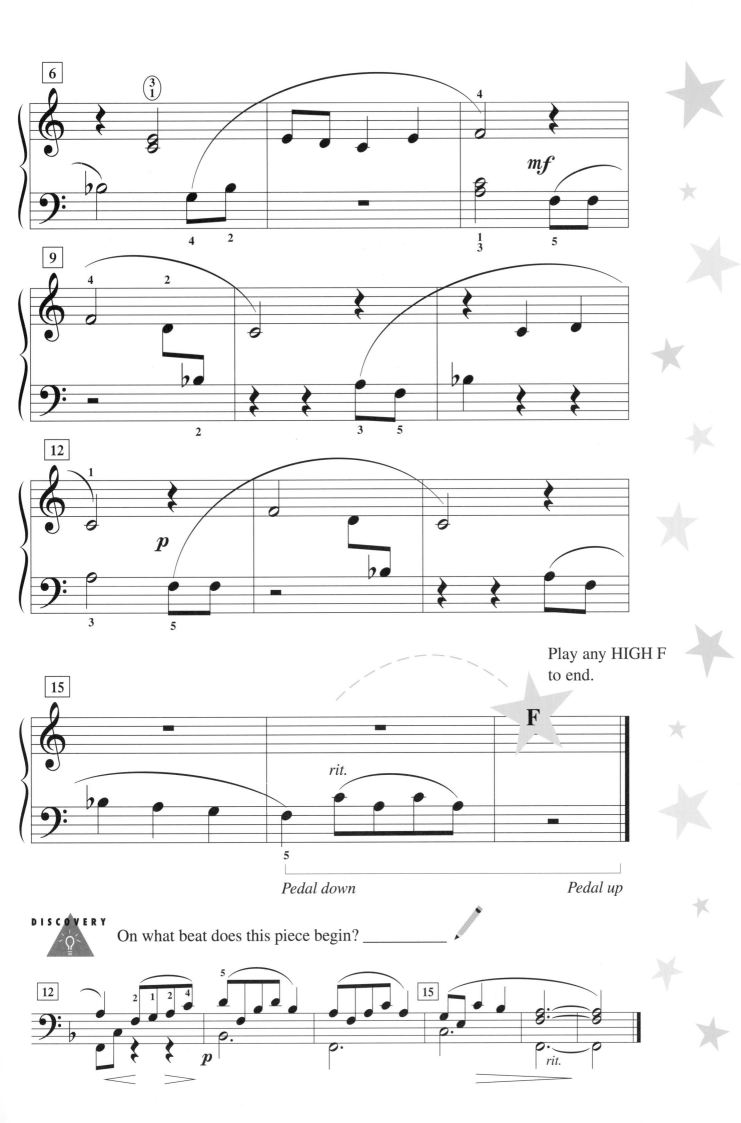

Play any HIGH F
to end.

Pedal down

Pedal up

DISCOVERY

On what beat does this piece begin? _____

21

Did you know...
Brahms supported his family as a child by playing in dance halls.

Brahms loved to read and eventually had over 800 books as an adult!

Brahms became so famous, he is now known as one of the 3 B's – Bach, Beethoven, and Brahms!

Mr. Brahms' Time Signature Game

1. Write ¾ or 4/4 before each bar of rhythm.

2. Now write 1 2 3 or 1 2 3 4 under the correct notes.

Brahms loved gypsy bands. Gypsy melodies and rhythms inspired his music.

Brahms wrote 4 symphonies that are among the greatest in orchestra music.

Brahms is buried beside Beethoven.

- Write in each **time signature**.
- Clap the rhythm with your teacher.
- Set a steady beat and sightread.

Gypsy Tunes!

Briskly

5   4   3

5 *f* Gyp - sies   are   danc - ing,   danc - ing,   danc - ing.

1

Gyp - sies   are   danc - ing,   to   the   gui - tars.

Moderately
(run-ning run-ning walk)

mf   5   2   1

5

2   3   4

Your teacher will play example **a** or **b**.
Listen carefully and circle the correct example.

LISTEN...

1a.

or

b.

2a.

or

b.

3a.

or

b.

4a.

or

b.

(Your teacher may ask you to sightread each example.)

Ice Cream
C 5-Finger Scale

Words by Crystal Bowman

Lively

I - cy, frost - y, twirl - y, swirl - y, tast - y on its cone.

Melt - ing, drip - ping, stick - ing, lick - ing fast - er till it's gone! Yum!

More Ice Cream

Here is the same piece using the **G 5-finger scale**.

Lively

I - cy, frost - y, twirl - y, swirl - y, tast - y on its cone.

Melt - ing, drip - ping, stick - ing, lick - ing fast - er till it's gone! Yum!

DISCOVERY Find and circle a **4th** for the R.H. in *More Ice Cream*.

Transposing

Playing the same piece using a different scale is called *transposing*.
The note names change, but the **intervals** stay the same.

Tick each box when you are ready.

- I can play this piece using the **G 5-finger scale**. **G** ☐
- I can transpose this piece to the **C 5-finger scale**. **C** ☐

Mr. Haydn's Theme*

G 5-Finger Scale

Hint: Reading the **intervals** and listening
to the sound will help you transpose.

Franz Joseph Haydn
(1732–1809, Austria)
arranged

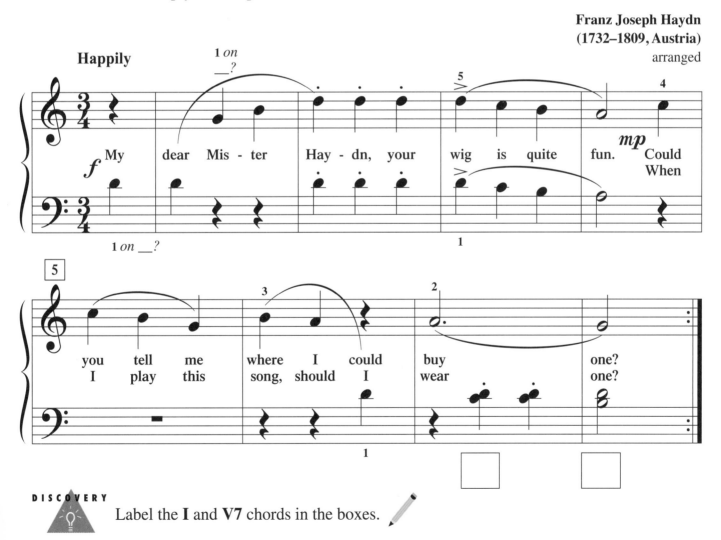

Happily

My dear Mis - ter Hay - dn, your wig is quite fun. Could
When

you tell me where I could buy one?
I play this song, should I wear one?

DISCOVERY
Label the **I** and **V7** chords in the boxes.

*from *Symphony No. 100, Finale*

- Complete the information
  for each of Haydn's themes.

Mr. Haydn's Themes to Transpose

1. a. Name the **intervals** in the boxes.
   b. Play as written.
   c. Transpose to the **G 5-finger scale.**

from Symphony No. 100

Ex. 2nd   3rd

2. a. Name the **intervals** in the boxes.
   b. Play as written.
   c. Transpose to the **C 5-finger scale.**

from Symphony No. 104

3. a. Name the **intervals** in the boxes.
   b. Play as written.
   c. Transpose to the **G 5-finger scale.**

from Symphony No. 30

26

Listen to Bach, Beethoven, and Brahms

- Close your eyes and listen.
  Your teacher will play a short melody by Bach, Beethoven, or Brahms.

- Then your teacher will play a **transposed melody**. The transposed melody will be the **same** (correctly transposed) or **different** (incorrectly transposed).

- Circle same or different for the second pattern you hear.

1.

Listen!

SAME

or

DIFFERENT

4.

Listen!

SAME

or

DIFFERENT

2.

Listen!

SAME

or

DIFFERENT

5.

Listen!

SAME

or

DIFFERENT

3.

Listen!

SAME

or

DIFFERENT

6.

Listen!

SAME

or

DIFFERENT

For Teacher Use Only

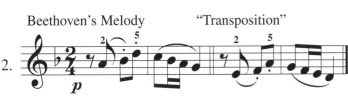

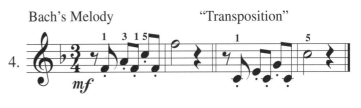

Warm-up

1. On the closed keyboard lid, play this R.H. finger pattern:

3 - 5 - 4 | 3 - 5 - 4 | 3 - 5 - 4 | 3

2. Optional: Explore gentle wrist circles as you play on the keys.
   (Circle down and out as you play from fingers 3 to 5, rising up and
   around to complete the circle. Teacher demonstrates.)

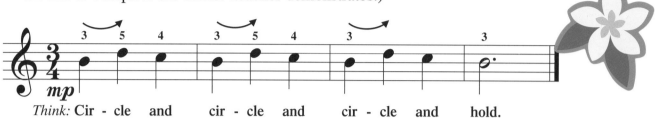

Think: Cir - cle and cir - cle and cir - cle and hold.

My Daydream

G 5-Finger Scale

Words by Crystal Bowman

Floating along

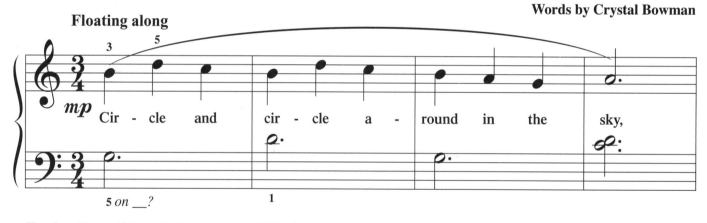

mp Cir - cle and cir - cle a - round in the sky,

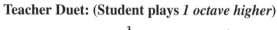

5 *on* __?

Teacher Duet: (Student plays *1 octave higher*)

CD 20-21   Tech & Perf page 5 (Making Rainbows)

5

birds glid - ing by, wish I could fly.

9

I'd go to plac - es that I've nev - er seen.

13

wrist floats off

Oh what a day for a day - dream.

Review: *8va* means to play one octave (8 notes) higher.

BOTH HANDS 8va higher- - - - - - - - - - - -

17

p

rit.

DISCOVERY

Transpose *My Daydream* to the **C 5-finger scale**.
What is the first L.H. note? _____   What is the first R.H. note? _____

New Dynamic Marks

Review: Dynamics refer to the loudness and softness of the music. $\boldsymbol{f}, \boldsymbol{mf}, \boldsymbol{mp}$, and $\boldsymbol{p}$ are dynamic marks you have learned.

crescendo (cresc.) ———————— means gradually **louder**.

diminuendo (dim.) ———————— means gradually **softer**.

Your teacher will help you pronounce *crescendo* and *diminuendo*.

Hold the sustaining pedal down throughout the entire piece!

The Clock Strikes Thirteen!
_____ 5-Finger Scale

Wrist float-off
to any HIGH G

9 Play the thirteen bells on a HIGH G of your choice.

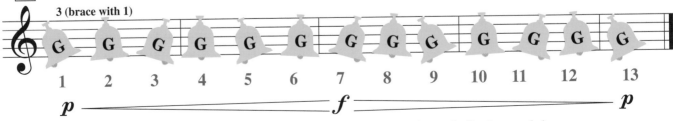

Begin as soft as possible and make a dramatic *crescendo* and *diminuendo*!

🔘 CD 22-23 ✍ Tech & Perf page 13

The Elf's Silver Hammer

_____ 5-Finger Scale

- Notice that both hands are written in the **treble clef**.

DISCOVERY Can you memorize this piece?
Can you transpose it to the **G 5-finger scale**?

Crescendo and Diminuendo
(cres-SHEN-do)   **(di-min-u-EN-do)**

- Practise pointing to the words and pronouncing them aloud.

crescendo (cresc.)   *diminuendo (dim.)*

gradually louder   gradually softer

- Draw a ⟨ or ⟩ under each picture to show how it would sound.

the bugle boys coming closer

Draw:

a horse-drawn carriage riding away

Draw:

a train disappearing in the night

Draw:

a traffic jam building up

Draw:

a helicopter landing in front of your house

Draw:

a kite drifting away in the wind

Draw:

• Sightread these melodies. Watch for the ⟨ and ⟩ markings.

• Then transpose each to the 5-finger scale suggested.

Transpose to the **G 5-finger scale**.

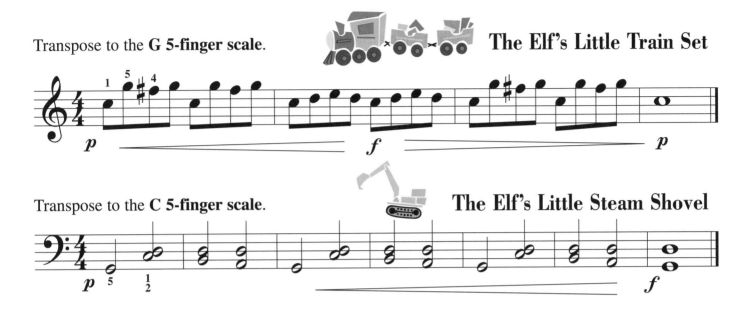

The Elf's Little Train Set

Transpose to the **C 5-finger scale**.

The Elf's Little Steam Shovel

 Your teacher will play a musical example.

Circle *crescendo*, *diminuendo*, or both *cresc.* and *dim.* for what you hear.

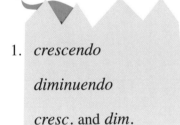

1. *crescendo*

   diminuendo

   cresc. and *dim.*

2. ⟨ and ⟩

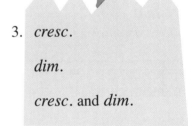

3. *cresc.*

   dim.

   cresc. and *dim.*

4. *crescendo*

   diminuendo

   cresc. and *dim.*

5. *cresc.*

   dim.

   cresc. and *dim.*

6. ⟨ and ⟩

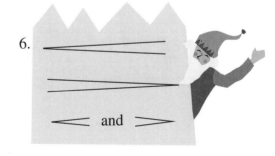

For Teacher Use Only: The examples may be played in any order.

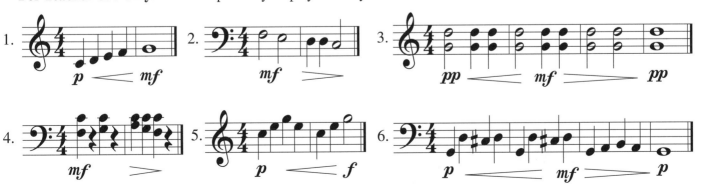

1. *p* ⟨ *mf*

2. *mf* ⟩

3. *pp* ⟨ *mf* ⟩ *pp*

4. *mf* ⟩

5. *p* ⟨ *f*

6. *p* ⟨ *mf* ⟩ *p*

33

3 UNIT · *phrase*

The Phrase

A *phrase* is a musical idea or thought.

A phrase is often shown in the music with a slur, also called a **phrase mark**.
Think of a phrase as a musical sentence and each note in the phrase as a word.

Shaping the Phrase

When we speak a sentence, our voice rises
and falls with expression.

• Use ⎯⎯< and >⎯⎯ to shape the phrases.
  The red and blue colours will guide you.

Ode to Joy

from the 9th Symphony

Ludwig van Beethoven
(1770–1827, Germany)
arranged

34 CD 26-27   Tech & Perf page 18

Can you play *bars 1-16* with your eyes on the music (not looking at your hands)?

Remember, a *phrase* is a musical idea.

• Draw phrase marks for the piece below.
  The dotted lines will give you a hint.

I Am the King

_____ 5-Finger Scale

Proudly

mf Once up-on a time, there | lived a king. | (I am the king. | I am the king.)

He was the king of | ev - 'ry - thing. | (I am the king. | I am the king.)

Ev-'ry morn-ing, he'd wake | up and sing, | "I am the king! | I am the king!

I am the king of | ev - 'ry - | thing!" (King of ev-'ry - | thing.)

rit.

CREATIVE Make up a new L.H. melody for *bars 1-2*. Keep the same rhythm, but choose any notes from the **G 5-finger scale**. Your teacher may demonstrate.

Two Interesting Facts about Phrases

Most piano music does NOT have words that point out the musical phrases.

Some music is composed of phrases, but phrase marks are NOT included in the music.

I Am the Phrase Finder!

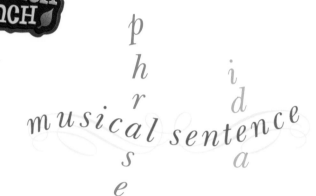

- Draw a semibreve rest in each empty bar. (There are 9.)

- Draw **phrase marks** in the music to show each "musical sentence."

- Sightread the music and listen for the **phrases**.

To end, repeat **bars 1-8.**

Phrase Warm-up

- Trace the ⟨ and ⟩ with a coloured pencil.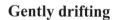

Moonlight Melody

Gently drifting

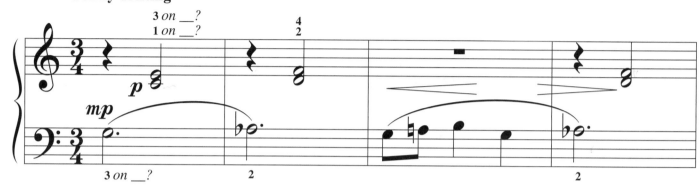

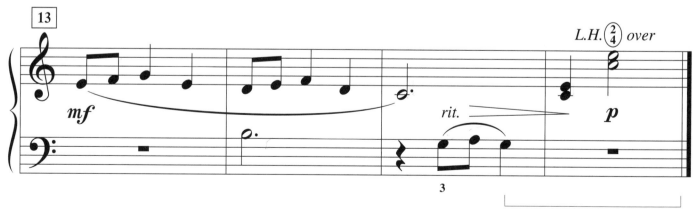

DISCOVERY

In which 2 lines of music does the L.H. have the melody? _____ and _____

You Can Compose!

C 5-Finger Scale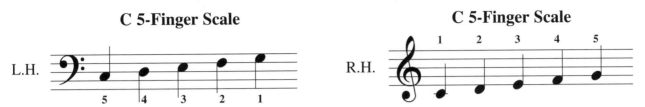

C 5-Finger Scale

L.H.

R.H.

- Complete this piece by choosing notes from the **C 5-finger scale**.
  Use the rhythm given above each bar.

- Then draw phrase marks and dynamic markings (*p*, *mp*, *mf*, *f*).
  Play your composition!

If You Meet an Alligator

Words by Crystal Bowman

rhythm:

R.H.

dynamic marking ___

If you meet an al - li - ga - tor, bet - ter run and let him be!

L.H.

Do not greet or try to calm him with a moon-light mel - o - dy.

R.H.

dynamic marking ___

But if you should find a bun - ny or a kit - ten or a mouse,

L.H.

You may pet it ver - y gen - tly, then bring it in - to your house!

Remember, from one key to the very *next* key
is a **semitone**.

• Find and play these semitones on the piano.
  Say aloud "semitone" as you play.

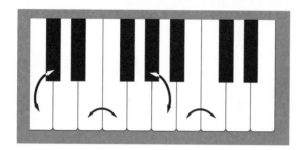

The Puppet Show

Quickly

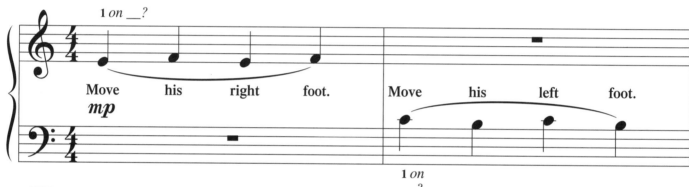

1 on __?

Move   his   right   foot.   Move   his   left   foot.

mp

1 on __?

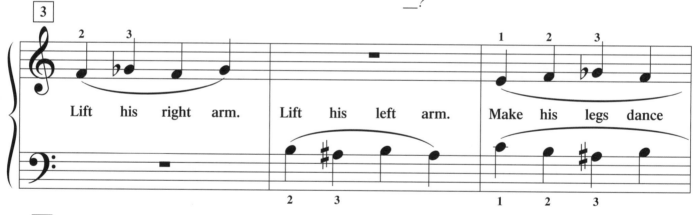

3

Lift   his   right   arm.   Lift   his   left   arm.   Make   his   legs   dance

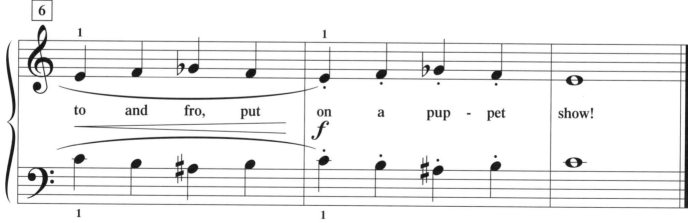

6

to   and   fro,   put   on   a   pup - pet   show!

f

DISCOVERY

After learning the music well, try playing it with your **eyes closed**!

Playful Puppets

• Complete the semitone challenge for each puppet.

What is a semitone UP from E?

_____
answer

Draw a 𝗈 a semitone LOWER.
Do you need a ♯ or ♭?

(you draw)

Circle the semitones. (There are 3.)

What is a semitone DOWN from
A? Do you need a ♯ or ♭?

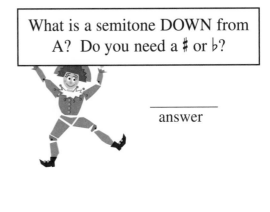

_____
answer

Draw a 𝗈 a semitone LOWER.
Do you need a ♯ or ♭?

Circle the semitone.

or

Write semitones going UP for
each little puppet.

going higher

Did you land
on G?

| C | C♯ | | | | | | |

41

Semitones and Tones
(Half Steps and Whole Steps)

A **tone** is made of 2 semitones.
Think of a **tone** as 2 keys—with one key in between.
Your teacher will demonstrate.

Tone Investigation

- Put an X on the key *in between* each tone shown below.

- Now play each **tone** on the piano.

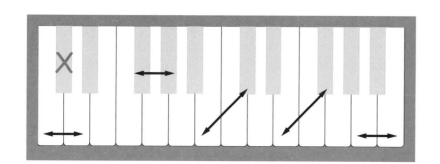

Our Detective Agency

Mysteriously

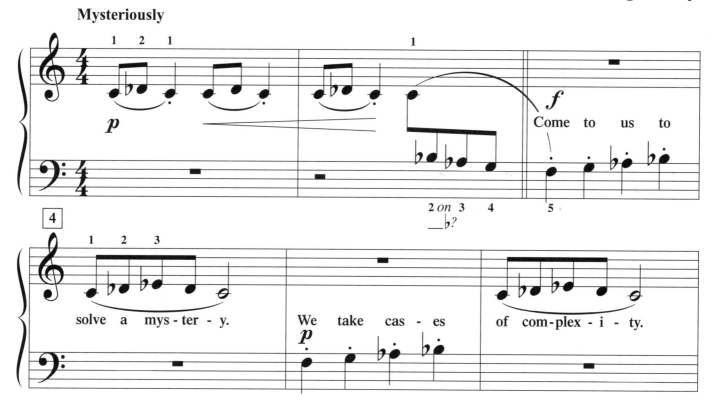

p Come to us to solve a mys-ter-y. We take cas-es of com-plex-i-ty.

Teacher Duet: (Student plays *1 octave higher*)

R.H.

L.H.

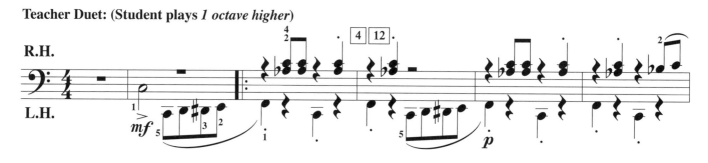

CREATIVE Begin on Middle C and play **tones** up the keyboard. Hold the pedal and listen!

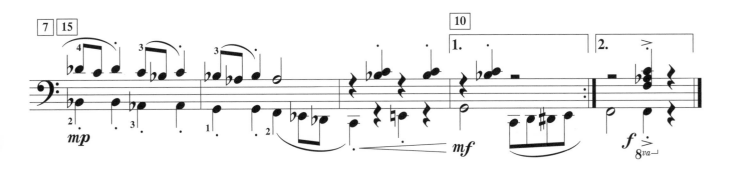

$\curvearrowright$ **fermata or pause mark**

Hold the note longer than its value.

Hold the sustaining pedal down throughout the entire piece.

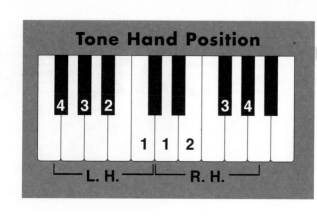

Tone Hand Position

Storms on Saturn

Dramatically swirling

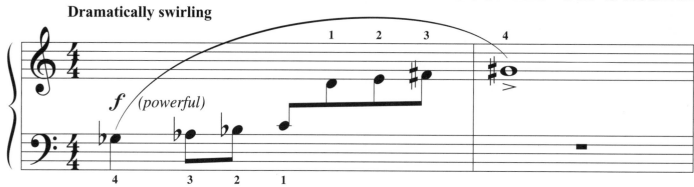

f (powerful)

p (like a whisper)

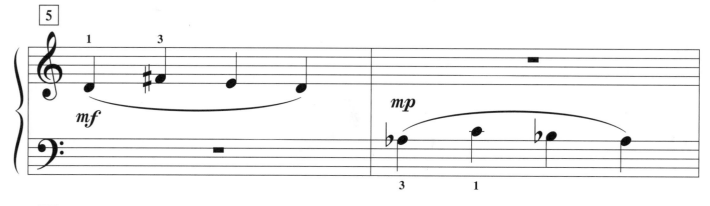

mf

mp

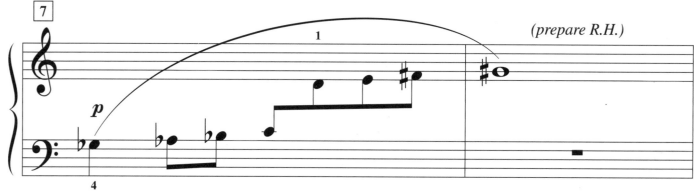

p

(prepare R.H.)

CD 36-37   Tech & Perf pages 23, 24-25

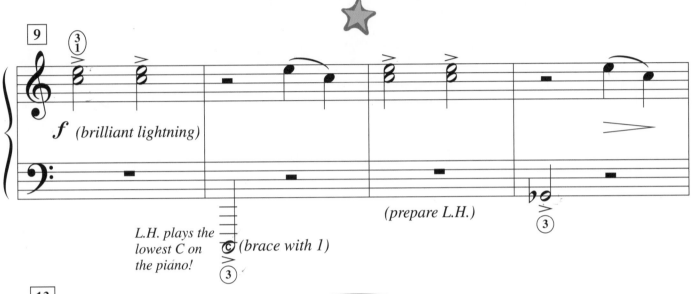

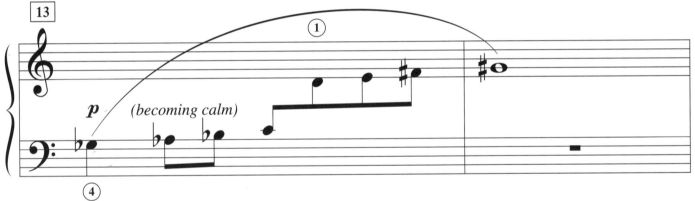

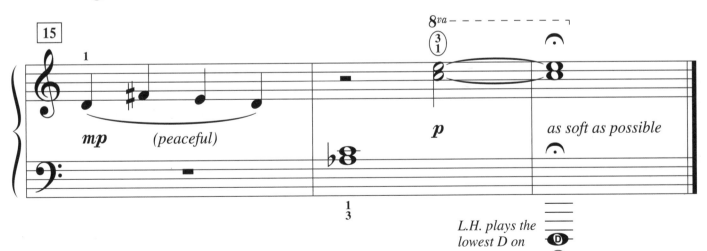

DISCOVERY The first phrase appears 4 times.
Draw a lightning flash by each one. The first phrase is *forte*.
What are the other three? _____

To **improvise** means to create "on the spot."
Improvise "moon shadow" music by doing the following:

- First, listen to your teacher play the accompaniment.
  Feel the mysterious mood.

- When you are ready, play notes from this tone pattern IN ANY ORDER.

- End by softly, playing all the R.H. keys together.

Moon Shadows Improv

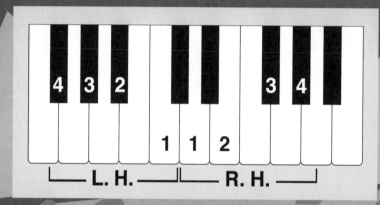

Did you know that Mars has two moons?

Teacher Improv Accompaniment: (Student improvises higher on the keyboard)
Moderately, mysteriously

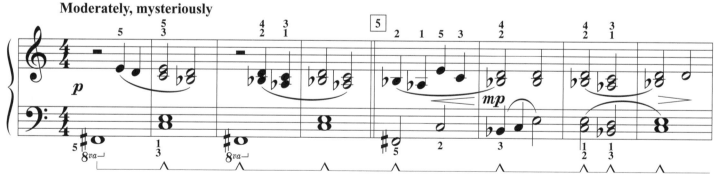

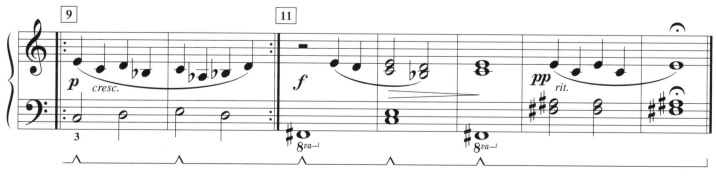

- Draw a line connecting each planet to its correct moon.

Planets and Moons

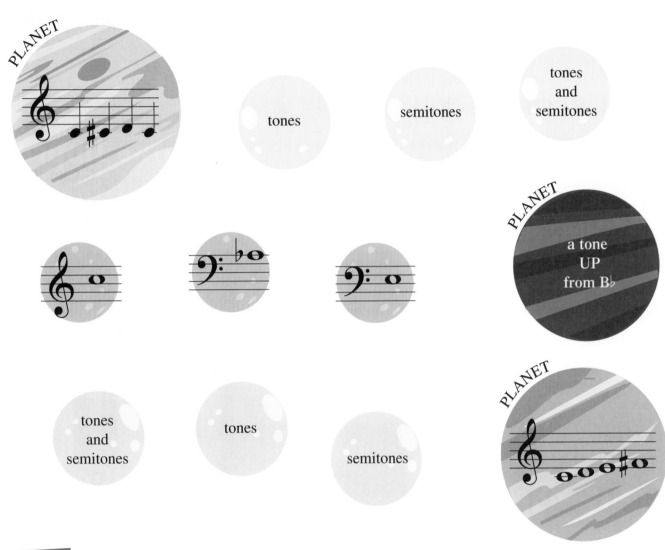

Your teacher will play either example **a** or **b**.
Listen carefully and circle the correct example.

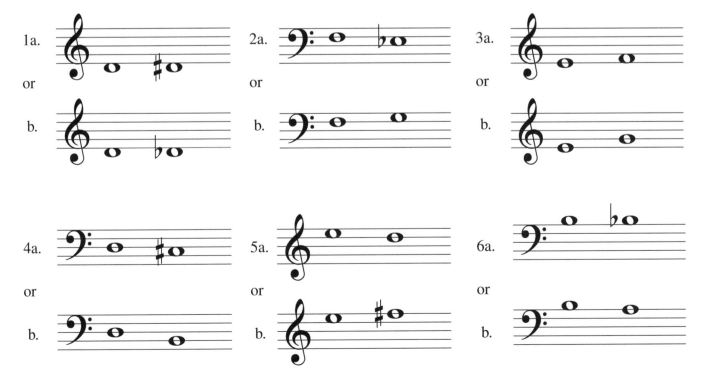

"Secret" Scale Formula

You already know C and G 5-finger scales. They use the tone and semitone pattern:

Tone – Tone – Semitone – Tone

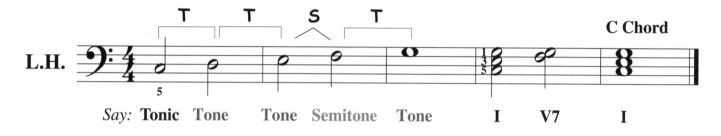

- Play and say the words above aloud. T=Tone   S=Semitone
- Now try the "secret" formula using the **G 5-finger scale**.

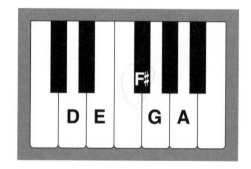

The D 5-Finger Scale

- To find the D 5-finger scale, play and say the **tone - tone - semitone - tone** pattern. Notice finger 3 rests comfortably on the black key.

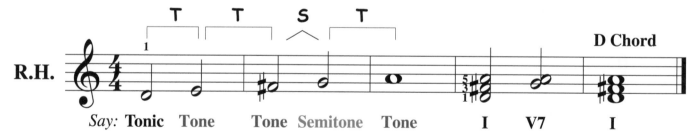

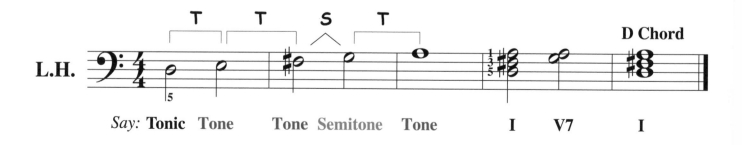

DISCOVERY Which fingers play a black key? _____ What is the name of the black key? _____ #

Hiking with Friends

Combining D and C Chords

Smoothly

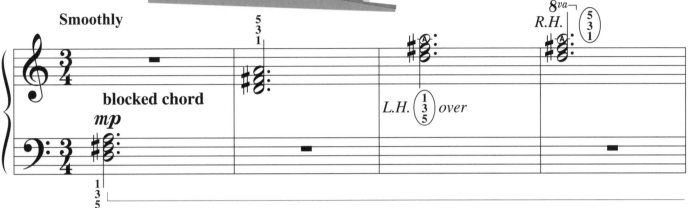

blocked chord

mp

5

broken chord

L.H. ⑤ *over*

lift

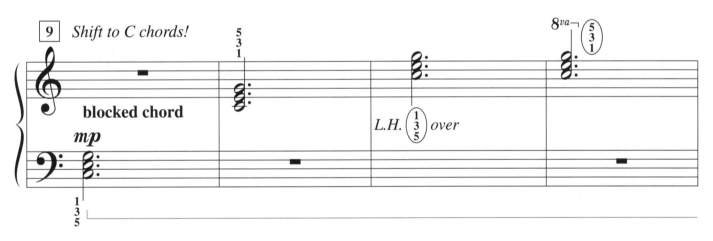

9 *Shift to C chords!*

blocked chord

mp

Repeat bars 1-8 to end.

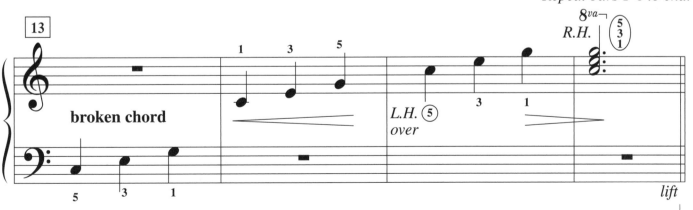

13

broken chord

L.H. ⑤ *over*

lift

DISCOVERY

Can you **memorize** this chord study?

This R.H. Old Man

D 5-Finger Scale

- Your teacher will help you with the L.H. cross-over in *bar 3*.

This L.H. Old Man

D 5-Finger Scale

DISCOVERY Transpose *This Old Man* to **C** and **G** 5-finger scales.

Writing the D Scale

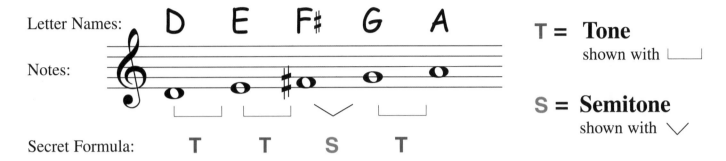

Letter Names: D E F♯ G A

Notes:

Secret Formula: T T S T

T = **Tone**
shown with ⌐_⌐

S = **Semitone**
shown with ∨

- For each stave, complete the letter names for the **D 5-finger scale** in the blanks.
- Next, write the missing semibreves on the stave.

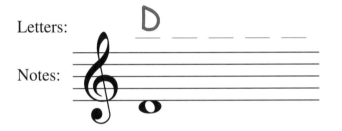

Letters: D __ __ __ __

Notes:

Letters: __ __ F♯ __ __

Notes:

Letters: __ E __ __ __

Notes:

Letters: __ __ __ __ A

Notes:

- Try the bass clef!

Letters: D __ __ __ __

Notes:

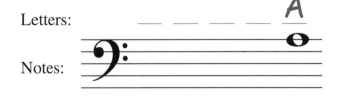

Letters: __ __ __ __ A

Notes:

Secret Formula Time
For each scale above, mark the **tones** with a bracket ⌐_⌐ and **semitones** with a wedge ∨ .
(See the top of the page.)

Rhythm Warm-up

- Tap and count the melody as shown.

Spring*

_____ 5-Finger Scale

Antonio Vivaldi
(1678–1741, Italy)
arranged

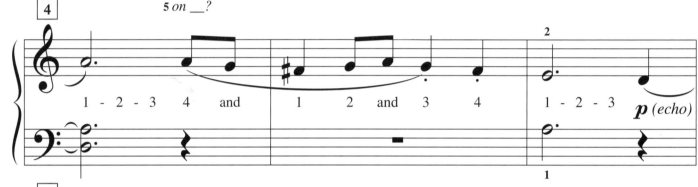

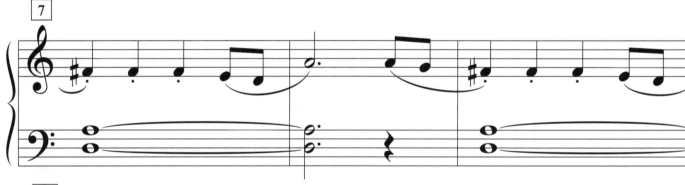

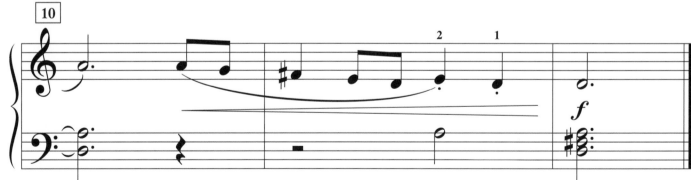

*from *The Four Seasons*

Teacher Duet: (Student plays *1 octave higher*)

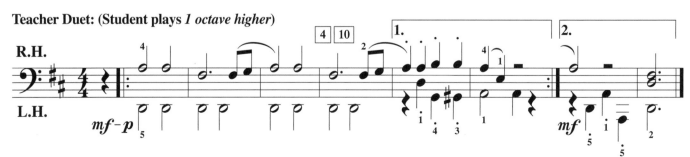

CD 42-43   Tech & Perf page 27

Vivaldi's Story

- Enjoy reading this short story about young Vivaldi.

Antonio's father was a barber, baker, and violinist. He taught his young son to play violin. Vivaldi grew up to become a priest and was called the Red Priest for his flaming red hair. For years, he taught at a girls' orphanage in Italy. People came from miles around to hear the beautiful music he wrote for the talented students. Vivaldi wrote over 500 concertos! A concerto is a piece for one or more instruments accompanied by an orchestra.

Intervals in the D 5-Finger Scale

- Write the intervals, then name both notes. Use only notes from the **D 5-finger scale**.
  Hint: Remember to include the **F♯**!

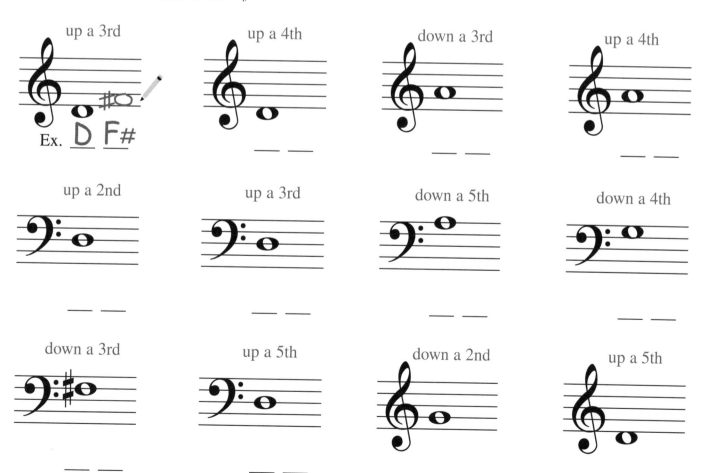

Pirate of the North Sea
_____ 5-Finger Scale

Lively (*Lightly bounce hand with a relaxed arm.*)

I'm the pi - rate of the North Sea. I'm brawn - y and strong. I'm the cap - tain of my fine ship. I sail all year long. I've

Teacher Duet: (Student plays *1 octave higher*)

R.H.

L.H.

CD 44-45

treas - ures from all a - round the world, dia - monds and gold! I'm the

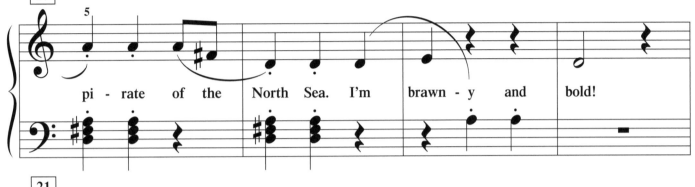

pi - rate of the North Sea. I'm brawn - y and bold!

DISCOVERY Circle the *pause* mark for the L.H. What does it mean to do?
Can you transpose this piece using the **C 5-finger scale**?

The Queen's Royal Entrance

This piece uses a hand shift between **C chords** and **D chords**.

Warm-up: Play back and forth between **D** and **C** chords.
Use left hand, then right hand.

CREATIVE Compose a piece that uses **D** and **C chords** all over the keyboard.
Call it *The Kitten's Playful Entrance* or a title of your choice.

The A 5-Finger Scale

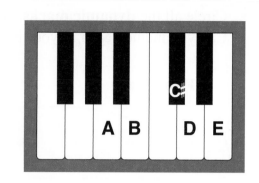

- Find the A 5-finger scale with the "magic formula."
  Notice finger 3 rests comfortably on the black key.

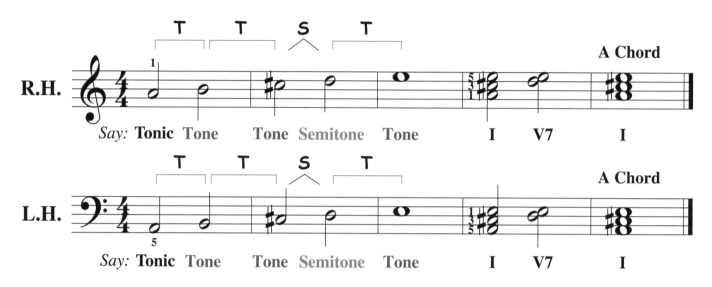

Hiking with Snacks

Combining A and G Chords

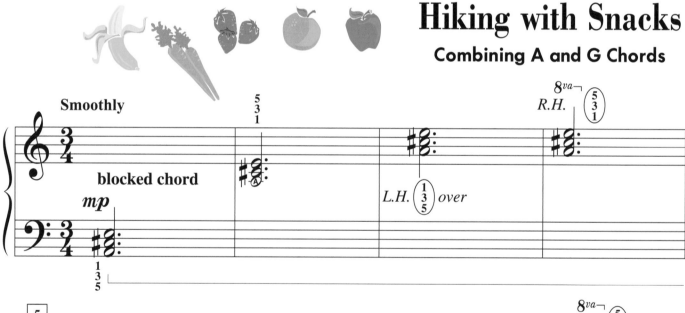

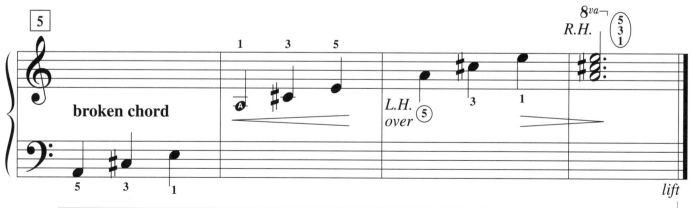

C R E A T I V E

Extend this piece by playing **G blocked** and **broken chords**. Then repeat using **A chords**.

- Circle all the **dynamic marks**.
  Can you include each in your playing?

Peter Pan's Flight

_____ 5-Finger Scale

Flying along

Writing the A Scale

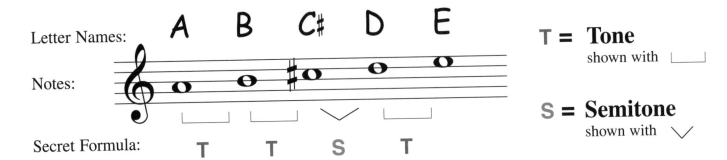

Letter Names: A   B   C#   D   E

Notes:

Secret Formula: T   T   S   T

T = **Tone**
shown with ⌐⌐

S = **Semitone**
shown with ∨

1. • For each stave, complete the letter names for the **A 5-finger scale** on the blanks.
   • Next, write the missing semibreves on the stave.

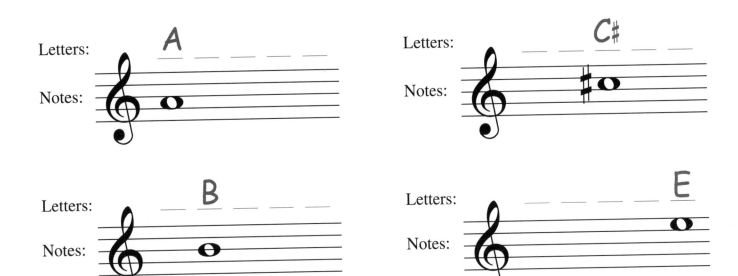

Letters: A _ _ _ _

Notes:

Letters: _ _ C# _ _

Notes:

Letters: B _ _ _ _

Notes:

Letters: _ _ _ _ E

Notes:

   • Try the bass clef!

Letters: A _ _ _ _

Notes:

Letters: _ _ _ _ E

Notes:

2. For each scale above, mark the **tones** with a bracket ⌐⌐ and **semitones** with a wedge ∨.
   (See the top of the page.)

60

Peter Pan's Key Flight

• Name the scales and chords that Peter Pan sees on his flight.

_____ scale

_____ chord

_____ scale

_____ scale

_____ chord

_____ chord

_____ scale

_____ chord

_____ chord

_____ chord

_____ chord

_____ chord

• Can you play each example on the piano?

L.H. Boogie Warm-up

- Practice the L.H. **boogie pattern** in *bars 1–2* until it's easy.

  Hint: Feel the semitone between **fingers 3** and **2**.

Boogie Woogie Band

___ 5-Finger Scale

CD 52-53   Tech & Perf pages 32-33

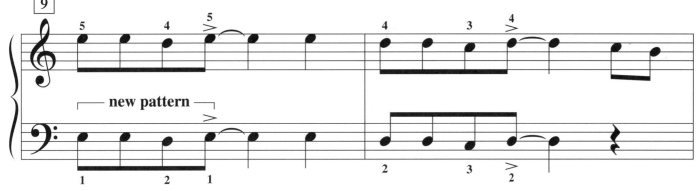

DISCOVERY

Play *Boogie Woogie Band* with the L.H. **one octave lower**.

Teacher Duet: (Student plays *as written*)

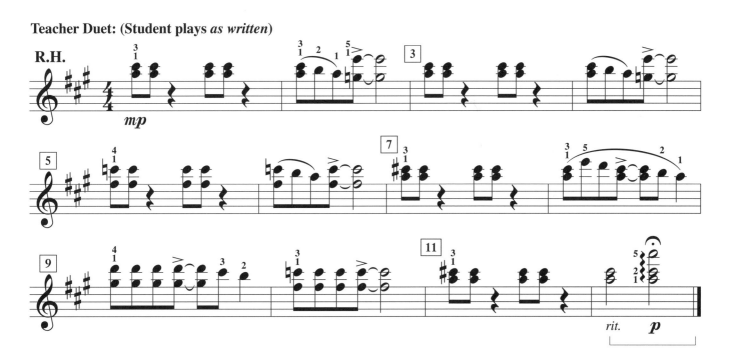

New: Leger Line E

- Cover up the notes to the left.
  Quiz yourself and name these notes.

C, D, and E are on short lines called **leger lines**.
E is one leger line higher than Middle C.

- Play these 3 notes saying the note names aloud.

Whirling Leaves

<u>A</u> 5-Finger Scale

Moderately fast

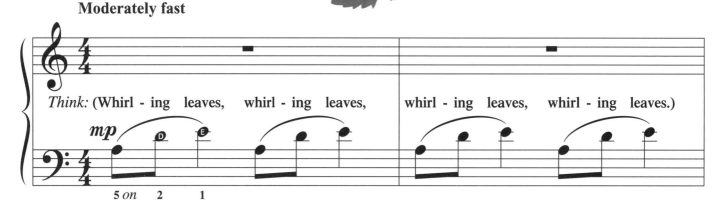

Think: (Whirl - ing leaves, whirl - ing leaves, whirl - ing leaves, whirl - ing leaves.)

mp

5 *on* 2 1
___?

3

4 *on* ___?

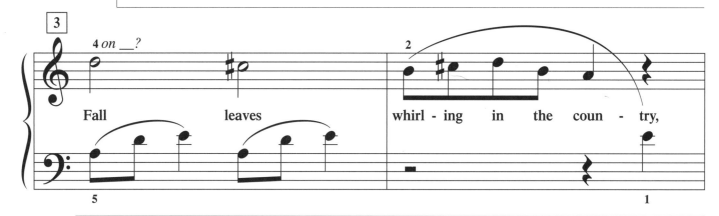

Fall   leaves   whirl - ing in the coun - try,

5   1

5

4

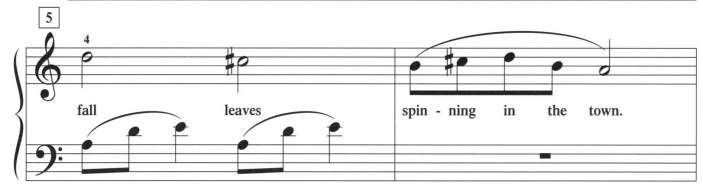

fall   leaves   spin - ning in the town.

CREATIVE Change the L.H. pattern to A-C-E using fingers 5-3-1. Change the R.H. pattern to all white keys, A-B-C-D-E. Now play the piece and make up a new title.

Remember, to **improvise** means to create "on the spot."

Improvise "whirling leaves" music by doing the following:

- First, listen to your teacher play the accompaniment.
  Feel the swirling motion of the music.

- With your R.H., begin playing notes from the **A 5-finger scale** IN ANY ORDER.
  Start with a very L-O-N-G note, then another L-O-N-G note.
  Gradually let your fingers move more quickly to other notes in the scale.

- To end, fade with the teacher duet.

Whirling Leaves Improv

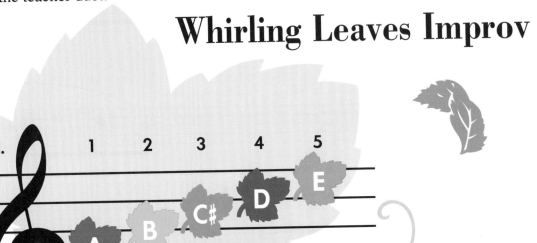

Teacher Improv Accompaniment: (Student improvises higher on the keyboard)

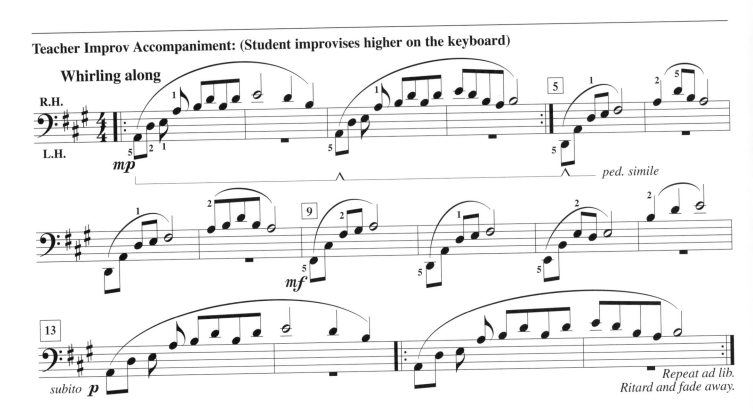

- Name the **chords** below. Hint: Look at the *bottom* note.
- Then name aloud the 3 chord notes. Hint: Go from the lowest to the highest note.

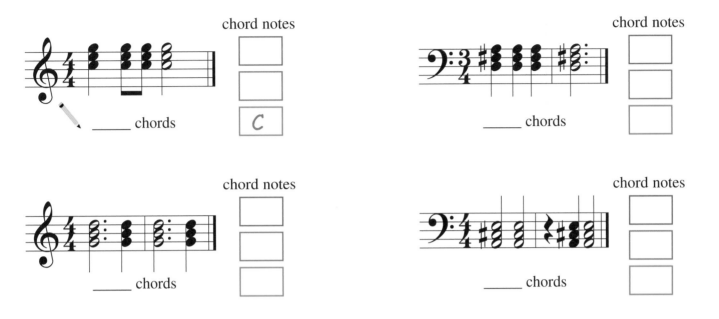

chord notes

_____ chords | C |

chord notes

_____ chords

chord notes

_____ chords

chord notes

_____ chords

Listen to the melody your teacher plays. Does it end on the **tonic** or **dominant**?
Circle the red or blue leaf for each example.
Hint: **Tonic** sounds like the end. **Dominant** sounds incomplete.

(circle one)

1. tonic step 1 / dominant step 5

2. tonic step 1 / dominant step 5

3. tonic step 1 / dominant step 5

4. tonic step 1 / dominant step 5

5. tonic step 1 / dominant step 5

6. tonic step 1 / dominant step 5

For Teacher Use Only: The teacher may change the order of examples, if desired.

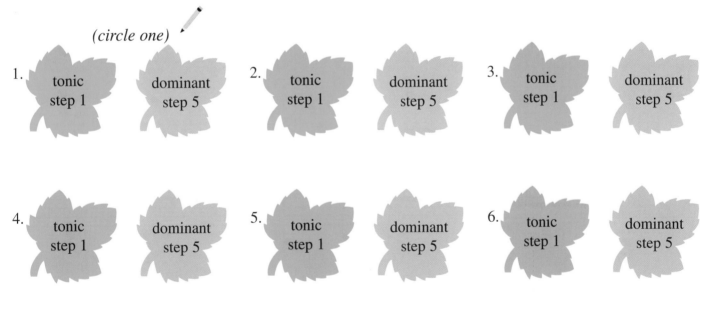

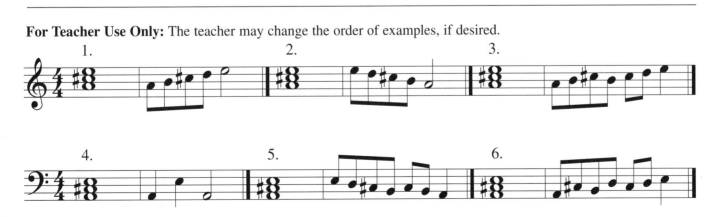

Major and Minor Sounds

You have learned C, G, D, and A 5-finger major scales.
The major pattern is **Tone - Tone - Semitone - Tone**.

1. Play the **C major** 5-finger scale.

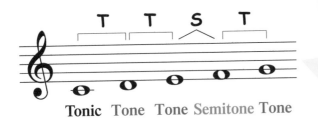

Tonic Tone Tone Semitone Tone

2. Now lower the 3rd note a *semitone*.

3. This is the **C minor** 5-finger scale. Play and listen to the sound.

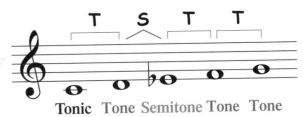

Tonic Tone Semitone Tone Tone

- **Practice** and **memorize** the *look, feel,* and *sound* of these 5-finger patterns.

Changing Moods

CD 56-57

The word **tempo** means the speed of the music—fast, slow, etc.

The tempo mark is located above the time signature. Italian words are commonly used as tempo marks. Your teacher will help you pronounce them.

Tempo marks

Allegro — fast and lively (♩ = **126–168**)

Moderato — moderately, slower than Allegro (♩ = **108–120**)

Andante — "walking speed," slower than Moderato (♩ = **76–104**)

Sword Dance

 **5-Finger Scale**

Teacher Duet: (Student plays *1 octave higher*)

CD 58-59   Tech & Perf pages 34-35

DISCOVERY Play *Sword Dance* using one of these tempo marks: *Allegro, Moderato,* or *Andante.*
See if your teacher can correctly name your tempo.

In an Old Castle

Secondo

Teacher Part

Ferdinand Beyer
(1803–1863, Germany)
original form

In an Old Castle

Primo

Am **5-Finger Scale**

Play BOTH HANDS 1 octave HIGHER throughout.
Notice the hands play in parallel motion.

Ferdinand Beyer
(1803–1863, Germany)
original form

DISCOVERY

Transpose *In an Old Castle* to **D minor**.

Major and Minor Sounds

Major Scale:
The semitone is between notes **3 and 4**.

Minor Scale:
The semitone is between notes **2 and 3**.

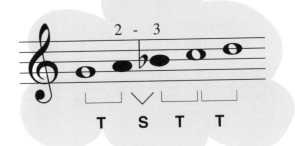

Changing Weather

1. • Circle the correct symbol for each example. MAJOR is ☀ and MINOR is ☁ .

   • Then write **major** or **minor** in the blank below.

a.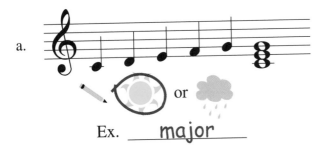

Ex. _____major_____

b.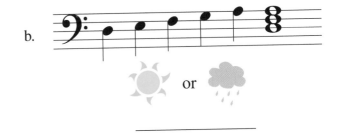

_____

c.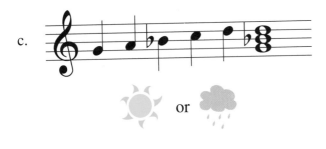

_____

d.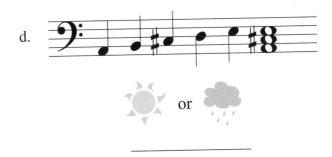

_____

e.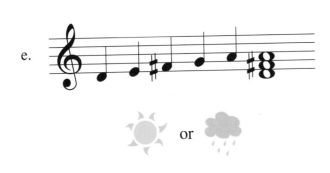

_____

f.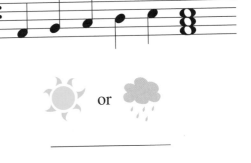

_____

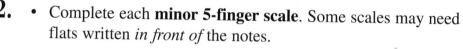

Minor Weather Change

2.
- Complete each **minor 5-finger scale**. Some scales may need flats written *in front of* the notes.

- Then mark the tones ⌞⌟ and semitones ∨ .

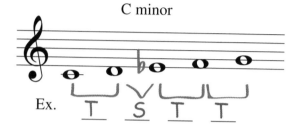

C minor

Ex. T S T T

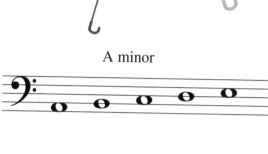

A minor

C minor

Do you need a ♭?

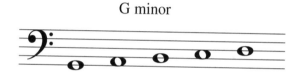

G minor

Write the Minor Scale

- Now write your own minor 5-finger scales. Add flats, if needed.
- Mark the **tones** ⌞⌟ and **semitones** ∨ .

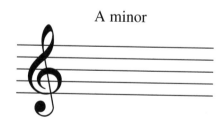

A minor

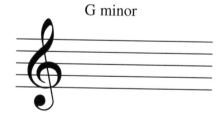

G minor

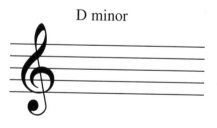

D minor

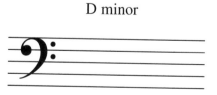

D minor

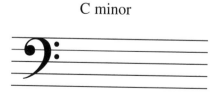

C minor

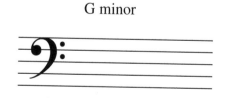

G minor

- Practise this piece playing *andante* before trying the *allegro* tempo mark.

The Horseman's Night Ride

C Minor 5-Finger Scale

CD 62-63

DISCOVERY How many beats does each **semibreve rest** receive in this piece? ___

Can you transpose *The Horseman's Night Ride* to the **G minor 5-finger scale**?

R.H. Warm-up (Imitate your teacher!)

Jazz Blast

_____ **5-Finger Scale**

DISCOVERY

Circle a **C minor chord** in this piece.

Teacher Duet: (Student plays _1 octave higher_)

Jazz Blast Improvisation

You are ready to improvise your own cool sounds for *Jazz Blast*. Here's how!

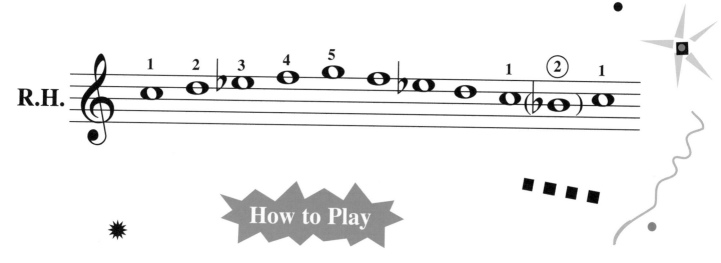

R.H.

How to Play

1. Use the C minor 5-finger scale, plus cross over to B♭!
   Play the keys in any order.

2. To start, set your R.H. over the keys and let your teacher begin.
   Feel the beat before you start playing.

3. Hint: Play lots of repeated notes, experiment with
   steps and skips, and play a few very l-o-n-g notes.

4. When your teacher says, "Now go back to *Jazz Blast*,"
   play *Jazz Blast* on page 78 once again to end.

Teacher Duet: (Student plays as shown)

- **Practise** and **memorize** the *look, feel,* and *sound* of these minor chords.

Hint: A small "m" = minor.

C Minor Hike

Cm (C minor)

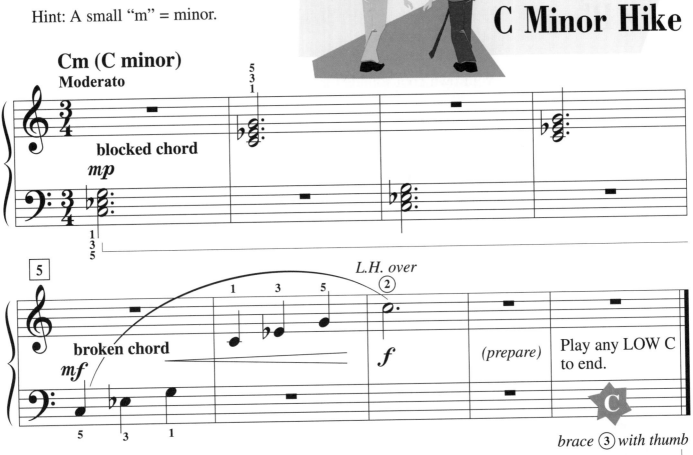

broken chord

brace ③ with thumb

(prepare) Play any LOW C to end.

G Minor Climb

Gm

broken chord

brace ③ with thumb

(prepare) Play any LOW G to end.

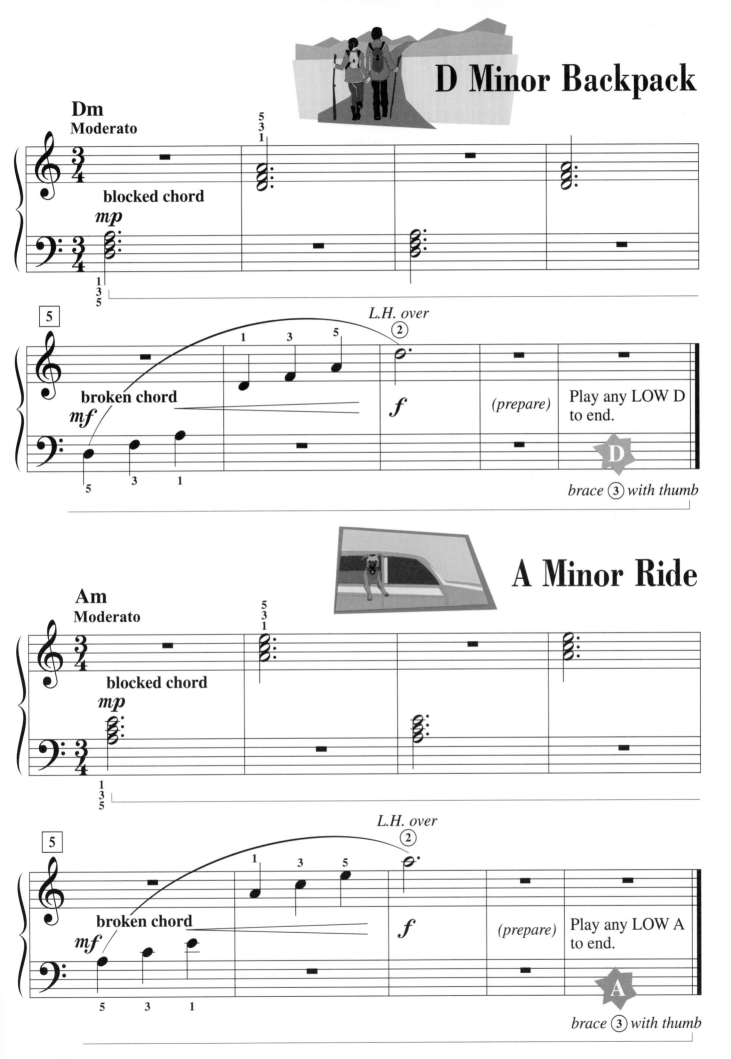

D Minor Backpack

Dm
Moderato

blocked chord

mp

broken chord

mf

L.H. over ②

f

(prepare)

Play any LOW D to end.

brace ③ with thumb

A Minor Ride

Am
Moderato

blocked chord

mp

broken chord

mf

L.H. over ②

f

(prepare)

Play any LOW A to end.

brace ③ with thumb

CREATIVE Choose one of these minor chords and make up your own **chord study**.

What's a Lead Sheet?

1.

In popular music, the **"lead"** means the melody.

2.

A **lead sheet** is the melody only with chord symbols written above the stave.

3.

A **chord symbol** is the letter name of a chord.

A capital letter means a major chord.

C = C major chord

A capital letter and a small "m" means a minor chord.

Cm = C minor chord

4.

Directions for page 83:

- First, play the melody until it's easy.

- Next, add **L.H. blocked chords** on beat 1 of each bar to match the chord symbols.

Chords for Go Tell Aunt Rhody

Play:

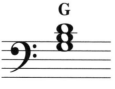

(G Major)

(G minor)

(D Major)

Lead Sheet for
Go Tell Aunt Rhody
G Major and G Minor

Andante

Traditional

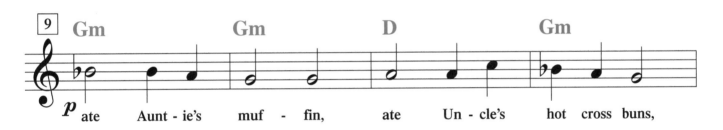

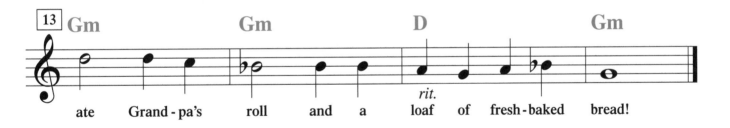

DISCOVERY Can you transpose *Go Tell Aunt Rhody* to the key of C?
Hint: The three chords will be **C major**, **G major**, and **C minor**.

Teacher Duet: (Student plays *as written*)

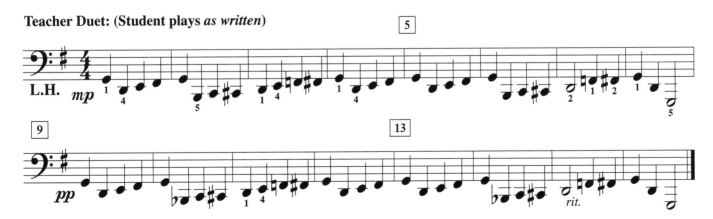

Snake Charmer

G Minor 5-Finger Scale

For a special effect, the R.H. 4th finger is raised to C♯ in this piece.

Moderato

Play 3 times!

(The snake rises up and down.)

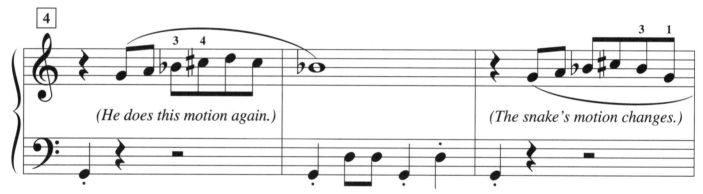

(He does this motion again.)   *(The snake's motion changes.)*

(He sinks back down.)

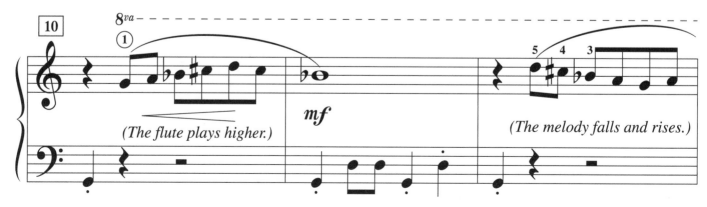

(The flute plays higher.)   *(The melody falls and rises.)*

(The snake twists to the music.)

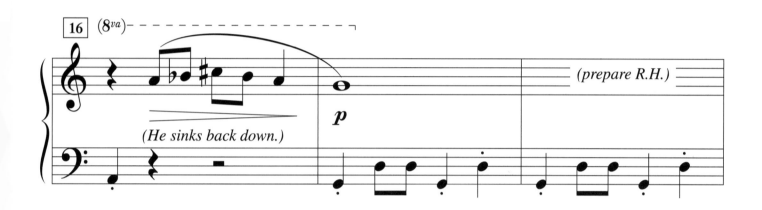

(He sinks back down.)

p

(prepare R.H.)

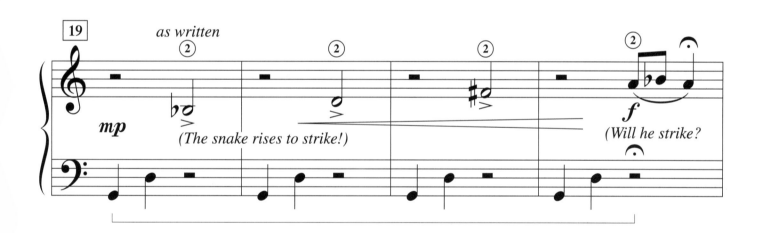

as written

mp

(The snake rises to strike!)

f

(Will he strike?

Whew! He sinks back down.)

mf

p

DISCOVERY Find three bars in the R.H. with this rhythm:

bar _____ , _____ , and _____ .

CHALLENGE SECTION

Teacher Note: The 12 major 5-finger scales shown below may be introduced throughout Level 2A. A final goal might be to play the *"Adventure Warm-up"* chromatically up the keys.

For Adventurers

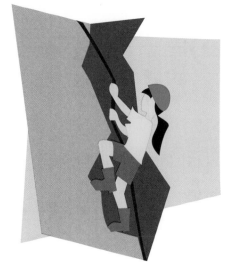

• Use the "Adventure Warm-up" below to explore each scale.

• Circle the keyboard for each scale learned.

• Transpose pieces from the book to these adventurous keys.

"Adventure Warm-up" in C

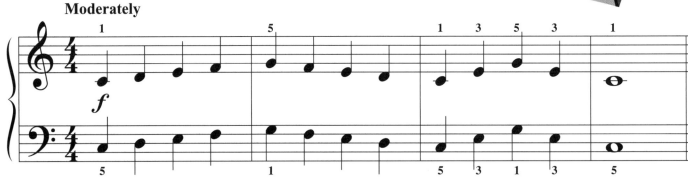

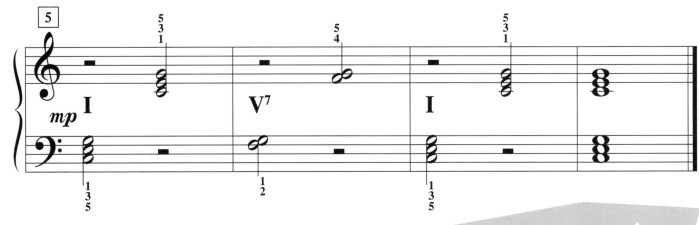

The **C, G,** and **F chords** are all white-white-white.

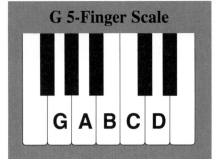

Ex.

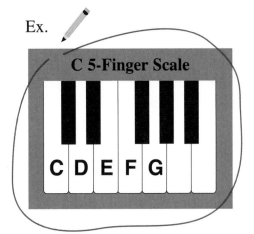

C 5-Finger Scale — C D E F G

G 5-Finger Scale — G A B C D

F 5-Finger Scale — F G A Bb C

86   Tech & Perf pages 42-47

The **D**, **A**, and **E chords** are all white-black-white.

D 5-Finger Scale

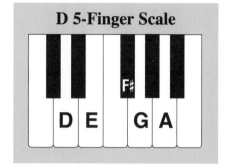

A 5-Finger Scale

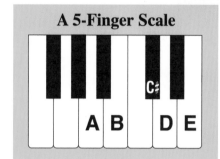

E 5-Finger Scale

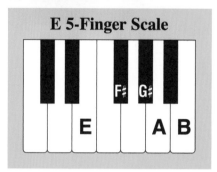

The **D♭**, **A♭**, and **E♭ chords** are all black-white-black.

D♭ 5-Finger Scale

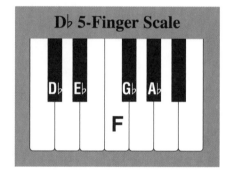

A♭ 5-Finger Scale

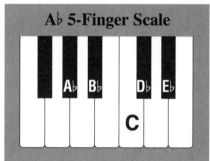

E♭ 5-Finger Scale

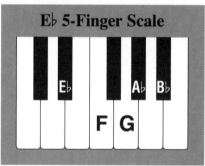

The **F♯** (or **G♭**), **B♭**, and **B chords** are all *different!*

F♯ 5-Finger Scale

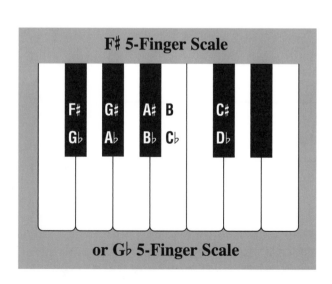

or **G♭ 5-Finger Scale**

B♭ 5-Finger Scale

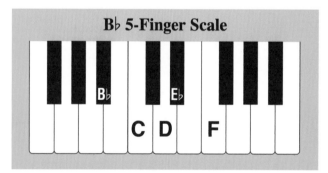

B 5-Finger Scale

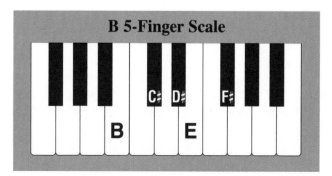

DISCOVERY On a separate sheet of paper, draw black and white mountaintops to illustrate the F♯ (or G♭), B♭, and B chords.

Piano Adventures® Certificate

Congratulations to:

____

(Your Name)

You have completed Level 2A
and are now ready for Level 2B.

LESSON & THEORY

TECHNIQUE & PERFORMANCE

Teacher: ____

Date: ____